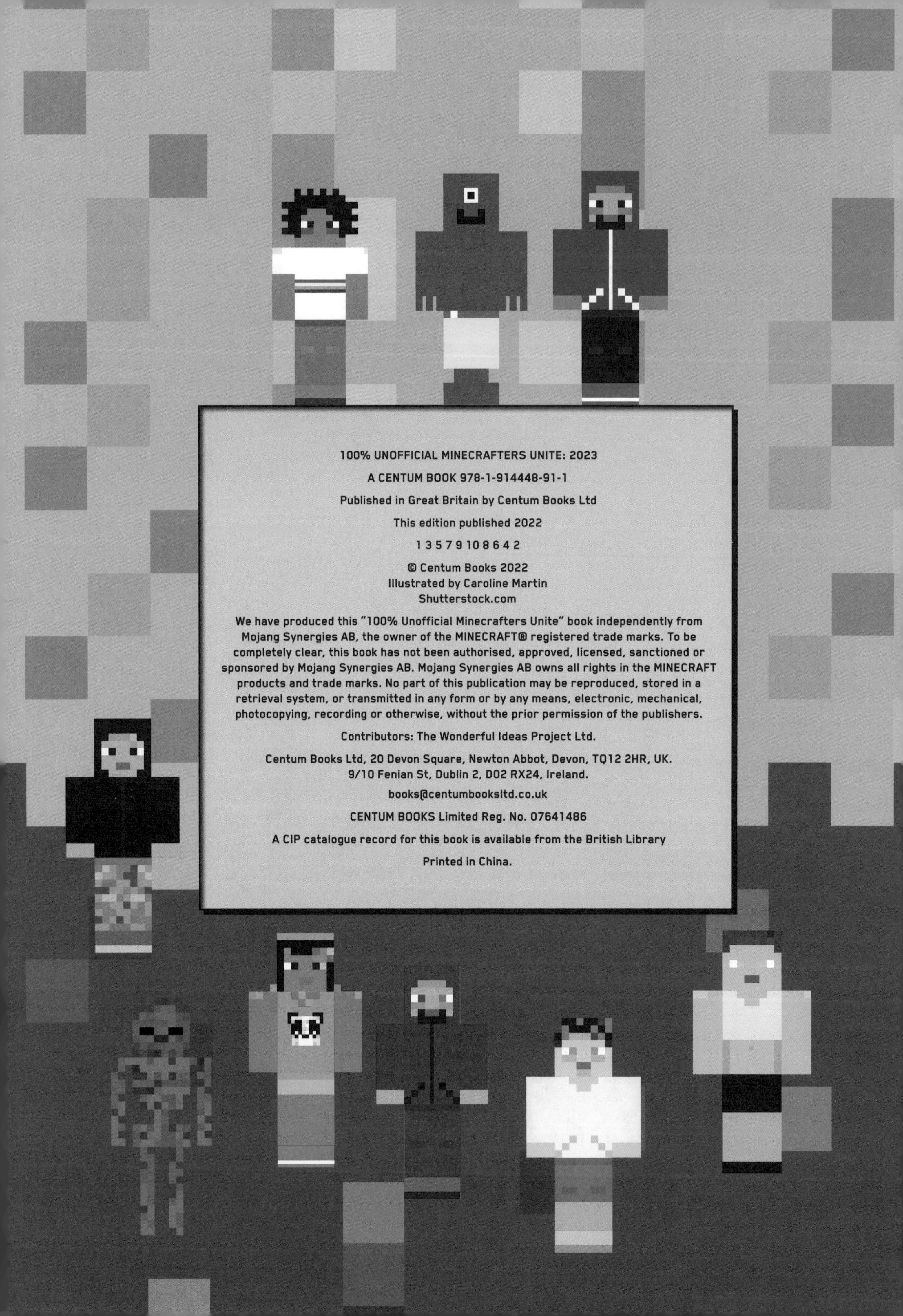

100% UNOFFICIAL MINECRAFTERS UNITE: 2023

A CENTUM BOOK 978-1-914448-91-1

Published in Great Britain by Centum Books Ltd

This edition published 2022

1 3 5 7 9 10 8 6 4 2

Illustrated by Caroline Martin
Shutterstock.com

Contributors: The Wonderful Ideas Project Ltd.

Centum Books Ltd, 20 Devon Square, Newton Abbot, Devon, TQ12 2HR, UK.
9/10 Fenian St, Dublin 2, D02 RX24, Ireland.

books@centumbooksltd.co.uk

CENTUM BOOKS Limited Reg. No. 07641486

A CIP catalogue record for this book is available from the British Library

Printed in China.

100% UNOFFICIAL

MINECRAFTERS UNITE

2023

centum

THIS BOOK BELONGS TO:

THOMAS

Use this blank template to create your character's look.

CONTENTS

GENERATING WORLD...

What world are you going to build? Or have you already built it? Come up with your unique world name, then use this space to think up some epic ideas.

CHOSEN WORLD NAME: PIZZA TOWN

YOUR WORLD'S BIOMES: Plains, Jungle, Ice Spikes, and Forest.

YOUR FIRST BUILD: Statue

BEST PLACE TO SHELTER: In a giant tree

FAVOURITE LOCATION: My house

PLANNED BIG BUILD: Geek Mansion

FAVOURITE MATERIAL: Orange Glazed Terracota

Jot down some words that describe your world – like busy, colourful or wild – then incorporate those words.

Look up real-world cities or countries and tweak the names to make them about you.

Use this grid to draw a map of your world.

Look around irl to figure out what kind of buildings and biomes you want to include!

Remember to build yourself a mine near to your shelter for easy access to materials.

When you spawn, the first thing to do is collect lots of wood!

DEEP MINE SEARCH

Go deeper than ever before and mine all the words in this huge grid.

- AXOLOTL
- AMETHYST
- AZALEA
- BIOME
- BUCKET
- CAVE
- COPPER
- CREEPER
- GLOW SQUID
- IRON
- MOBS
- MOSS
- PICKAXE
- REDSTONE
- SANDSTONE
- SILVERFISH
- SKELETON
- SPAWN
- WOOD

O	H	D	Z	U	J	J	S	F	F	L	A
K	P	D	G	F	D	C	B	F	R	H	K
U	P	I	E	V	A	C	V	E	F	Z	F
S	X	S	D	R	E	P	P	O	C	W	O
D	S	O	B	G	A	E	H	O	B	Y	U
X	R	U	D	T	E	J	J	G	I	D	R
R	E	P	M	R	L	Q	P	V	O	N	I
D	Y	H	C	T	A	J	I	N	M	V	C
U	O	U	V	K	Z	K	W	P	E	J	O
C	W	J	D	D	A	H	C	J	L	M	T
J	R	I	Y	J	X	Q	N	T	T	X	S
E	C	R	L	R	Q	G	O	E	G	V	Y
L	X	N	X	P	A	L	K	O	T	T	H
W	X	D	O	C	O	C	P	J	P	E	T
A	D	M	B	X	U	J	I	Z	G	L	E
I	L	K	A	B	X	P	M	J	O	A	M
R	T	J	F	P	Z	G	R	W	Y	L	A
T	I	D	U	F	H	S	X	O	T	X	C

HARDCORE HINT

Search left, right, up, down, diagonally, forwards and backwards. No words are split across both pages.

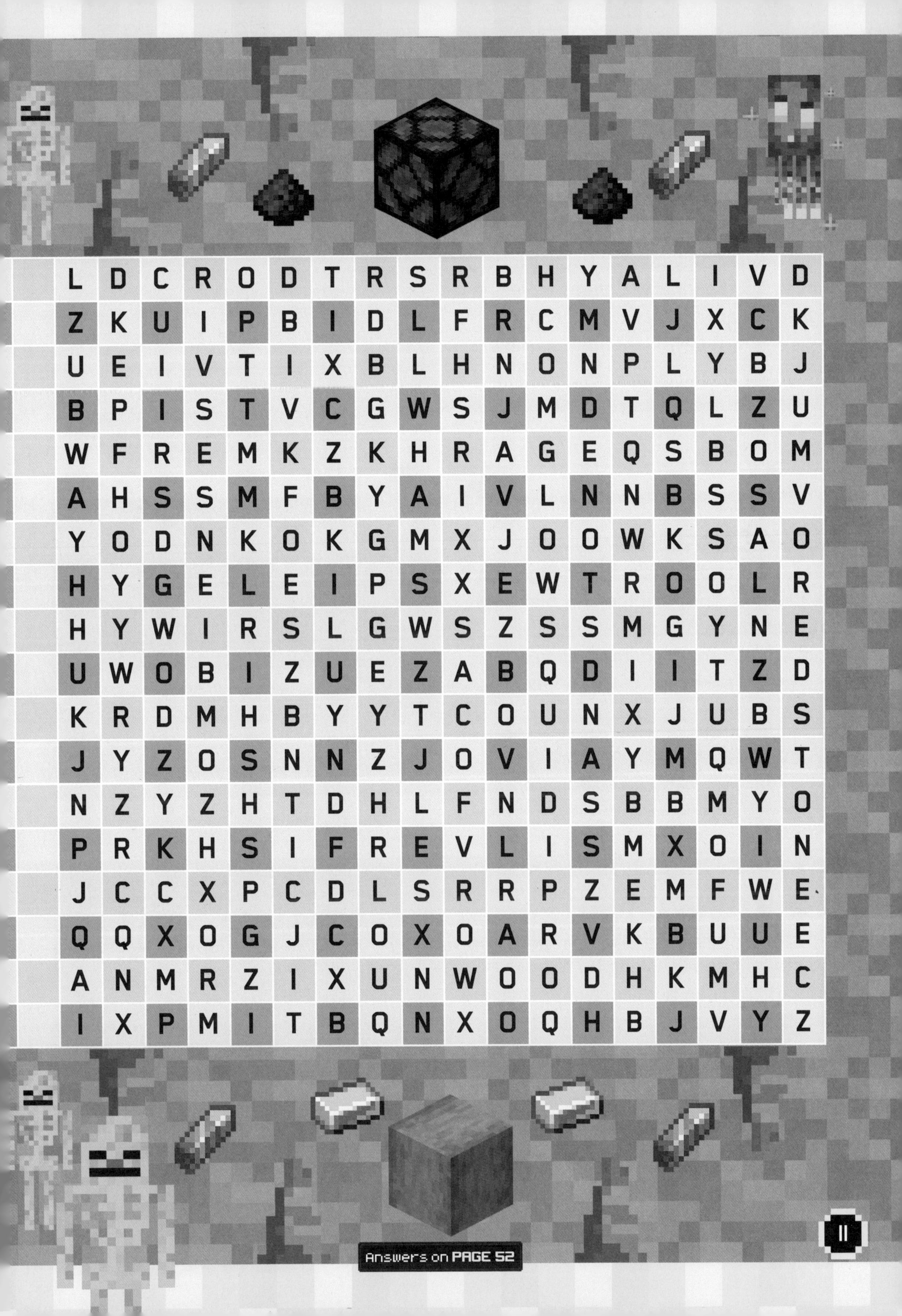

L	D	C	R	O	D	T	R	S	R	B	H	Y	A	L	I	V	D
Z	K	U	I	P	B	I	D	L	F	R	C	M	V	J	X	C	K
U	E	I	V	T	I	X	B	L	H	N	O	N	P	L	Y	B	J
B	P	I	S	T	V	C	G	W	S	J	M	D	T	Q	L	Z	U
W	F	R	E	M	K	Z	K	H	R	A	G	E	Q	S	B	O	M
A	H	S	S	M	F	B	Y	A	I	V	L	N	N	B	S	S	V
Y	O	D	N	K	O	K	G	M	X	J	O	O	W	K	S	A	O
H	Y	G	E	L	E	I	P	S	X	E	W	T	R	O	O	L	R
H	Y	W	I	R	S	L	G	W	S	Z	S	S	M	G	Y	N	E
U	W	O	B	I	Z	U	E	Z	A	B	Q	D	I	I	T	Z	D
K	R	D	M	H	B	Y	Y	T	C	O	U	N	X	J	U	B	S
J	Y	Z	O	S	N	N	Z	J	O	V	I	A	Y	M	Q	W	T
N	Z	Y	Z	H	T	D	H	L	F	N	D	S	B	B	M	Y	O
P	R	K	H	S	I	F	R	E	V	L	I	S	M	X	O	I	N
J	C	C	X	P	C	D	L	S	R	R	P	Z	E	M	F	W	E
Q	Q	X	O	G	J	C	O	X	O	A	R	V	K	B	U	U	E
A	N	M	R	Z	I	X	U	N	W	O	O	D	H	K	M	H	C
I	X	P	M	I	T	B	Q	N	X	O	Q	H	B	J	V	Y	Z

Answers on PAGE 52

CAVES + MOUNTAINS

CAVES

NOISE CAVES generate underground and come in two varieties: cheese and spaghetti. Cheese caves have wide-open areas filled with stone pillars, and spaghetti caves are long, narrow, and winding.

Some Noise Caves contain aquifers – flooded cave systems containing an abundance of ores.

LUSH CAVES are filled with vines, fruit and flowers that hang from the ceilings. They are the only place you can find Spore Blossom – pink flower blocks that hang from the ceiling and emit green particles.

To find a Lush Cave, look for azalea trees on the surface. These can indicate there are Lush Caves below.

Lush Caves are home to glow berries that can be eaten if you feel like it, but sometimes it's handy to leave them as they provide a light source for the cave.

DRIPSTONE CAVES have stalactites (hanging from the ceiling) and stalagmites (sticking up from the ground). You can find more copper ore here than in normal caves.

Falling onto a spike of Dripstone on the floor will damage you, so tread carefully!

Stalactites drip water and you can use a bucket to collect it. This gives you a renewable source of water! They also drip lava, which you can collect in a cauldron.

MOUNTAINS

You'll know you've found Mountain Meadows by the amount of flowers – and therefore bees!

MOUNTAIN MEADOWS can be found in Y-level 100 to 140 in mountains. Here you can find sweet berry bushes, cornflowers and dandelions growing in the soil. But no trees will grow here. They are the only mountainous area where villages can generate naturally.

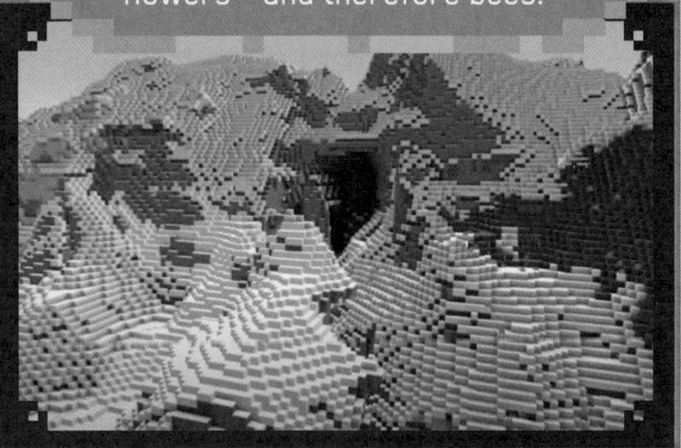

Mountain Meadows are some of the best places to find lilies, tulips and many more beautiful flowers.

This is the best place to find snow, snow blocks and powder snow on the ground!

MOUNTAIN GROVES are found on the lower slopes of mountains if they're between Y-level 110 and 140. This biome has rabbits, wolves and foxes running around a forest of spruce trees.

JAGGED PEAKS is the name for any set of mountain blocks above Y-level 170. If the area is cold, they will be **FROZEN PEAKS.** There is no life here!

Cross out the letter pairs and rearrange the remaining letters to complete the name of a passive aquatic mob endemic to the lush caves biome.

H X R S W S L O B R B T H W A

_ _ O _ _ _ L

Answer on PAGE 52

TAKING SHELTER

Sometimes a plain-old square house just won't cut it. Take a look at the suggestions below and get inspired to become a block-busting builder. Use the grid opposite to plan it and work out what you need.

- A moss-covered cave
- A mountain-top lair
- A treehouse
- A castle
- An underwater base
- A hill fort
- A floating house
- An underground house
- A beach house
- A log cabin in the woods
- A mansion

YOU MAY WANT YOUR SHELTER TO HAVE:

- STORAGE SPACE
- AN ENTRANCE TO YOUR MINE
- ROOM FOR YOUR BED
- A CRAFTING AREA
- A SMELTING AREA
- A FARM FOR FOOD
- SPACE TO BREW POTIONS
- AN ENCHANTING AREA

WHAT AM I?

WHAT AM I?

To find me go down as far as you can, until you hit bedrock. Use me to make high-tier tools, armour, or even a jukebox.

Answers on PAGE 52

What else would you include?
HOME SWEET HOME

RACE TO THE END

Play against a friend and journey to The End! Who will be first to reach the portal room and activate the end portal?

MULTIPLAYER MODE

START

1

2

3

4

5 YOU'VE GIVEN YOURSELF A JUMP BOOST! JUMP FORWARD 2 SQUARES.

6

22

23

24

25

26

27

28

29

30

31

32 YOU FOUND SOME FOOD AND HAVE A HEALTH BOOST. MOVE FORWARD 4 SQUARES.

33

34

35

36

52

53 YOU'RE LOST IN A DEEP CAVE SYSTEM. MISS A TURN.

54

55

56

57

58

59

60

61

62 A ZOMBIE HAS ATTACKED YOUR VILLAGE! GO BACK 2 SQUARES.

63

64

65

66

WHAT TO DO:

- Find two coins to use as counters, and a dice.
- Choose one player to start, and then take turns to roll the dice.
- Move forward the number of spaces shown on the dice. If you land on a square with instructions, follow the directions.
- The first player to reach the Portal Room is the winner!

LAUGH YOUR BLOCKS OFF!

Here are some great gags to entertain your friends!

MY FRIEND WAS MINING WITH A PICKAXE.
Luckily his injuries were . . . minor.

HOW DO YOU CUT DOWN A TREE IN MINECRAFT?
How WOOD I know?

WHAT'S SO GOOD ABOUT COBBLESTONE?
It's hand-PICKED!

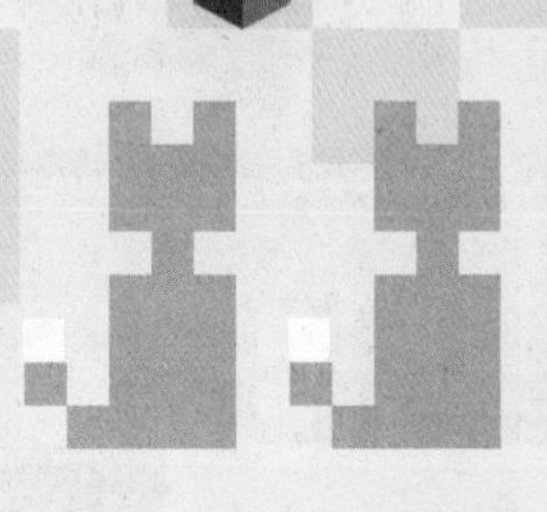

WHAT DO YOU GET IF YOU SPAWN A LOT OF KITTENS?
A meowtain!

HOW DO CRAFTERS AVOID SUNBURN?
Sunblock

WHY COULDN'T THE VILLAGER BREAK THE BEDROCK?
It was just too hard.

WHAT DID THE VILLAGER SAY WHEN HE GOT BACK FROM THE CAVE?
It was ore-ful!

SKELETON SILLIES!

HOW DO YOU MAKE A SKELETON LAUGH?
Tickle its funny bone!

WHO WON THE SKELETON BEAUTY CONTEST?
No body!

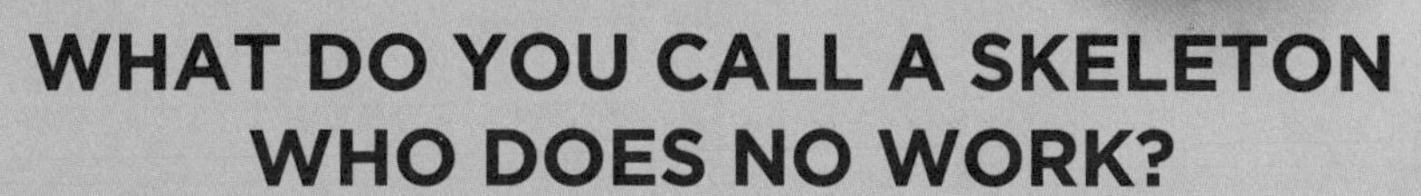

WHAT DO YOU CALL A SKELETON WHO DOES NO WORK?
A lazy bones!

HA HA

WHAT IS A SKELETON'S FAVOURITE INSTRUMENT?
A trom-bone!

WHY COULDN'T THE SKELETON CROSS THE ROAD?
It didn't have the guts!

WHY DIDN'T THE SKELETON GO TO THE PROM?
Because it had no body to dance with!

PACK UP!

You need to get packed up for a mining adventure!
Tick the eight most useful items.

Now put a cross against the four LEAST useful!

Can you spot 5 differences between these pictures of passive mobs?

Answers on **PAGE 52**

TOP THREE

There is so much to do in Minecraft.
Write down your top three in the categories below:

BOOM

TOOLS:

1 Netherite axe
2 Diamond Pickaxe
3

WEAPONS:

1
2
3

PETS:

1
2
3

ORES TO MINE:

1
2
3

BIOMES TO LIVE IN:

MATES TO GAME WITH:

Unscramble the letters to reveal three mobs that can be tamed.

Answers on PAGE 52

THE PATH TO SURVIVAL

Can you mine your way through this mega-hard maze, avoiding the baddie mobs and collecting items for survival as you go? No cheats, no respawning. Make it through or it's game over!

START

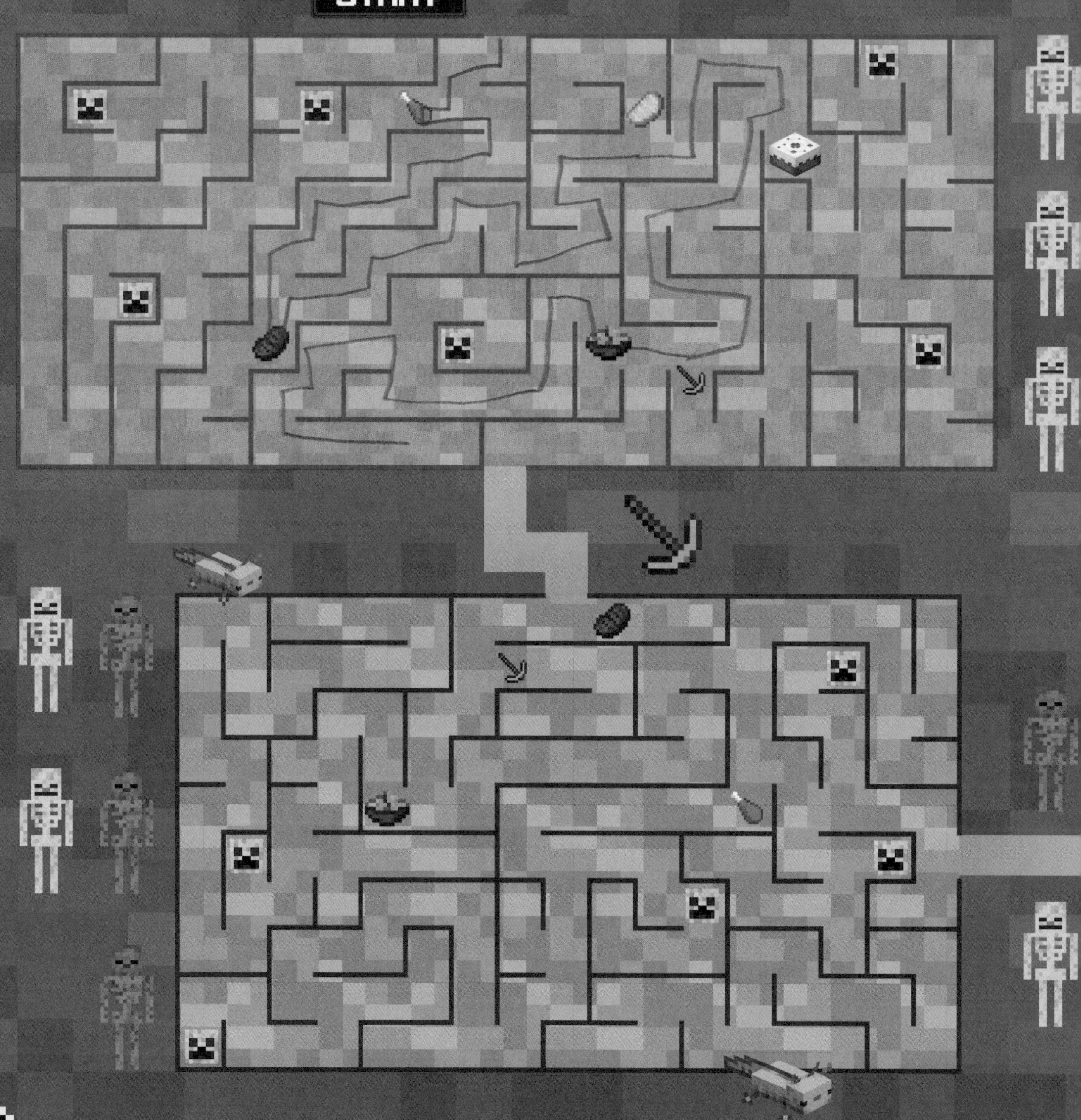

Answer on PAGE 52

MASTER BUILDERS

There are lots of things to remember when you are constructing. Follow these tips to make sure that your buildings are the best.

Make a good plan, maybe on paper, before you start. Planning is everything.

BUILD WITH OBSIDIAN AS IT CAN'T BE DESTROYED EASILY.

Use a night activating lava trap to defend your home.

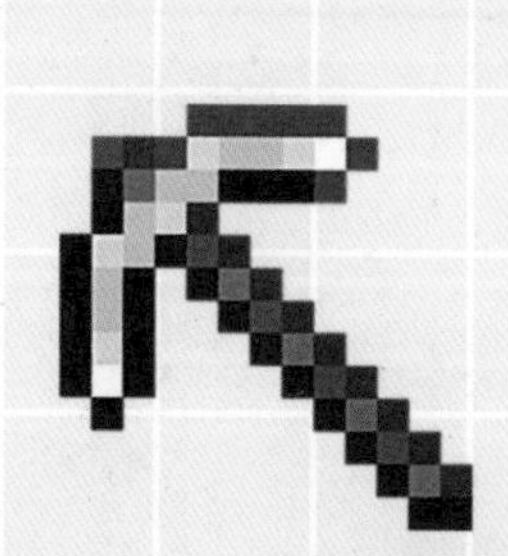

ADD PILLARS TO YOUR WALLS TO GIVE THE ROOMS OF YOUR BUILDING MORE PERSONALITY.

Start laying out your design on the ground first by digging holes and adding slabs of the block type you will use for each part of your build.

KEEP A CHEST BY YOUR DOOR, SO YOU CAN GATHER UP ESSENTIALS BEFORE HEADING OUT.

FOR EXTRA SECURITY BUILD USING THREE-LAYERED WALLS, WITH THE MIDDLE ONE BEING OBSIDIAN OR WATER.

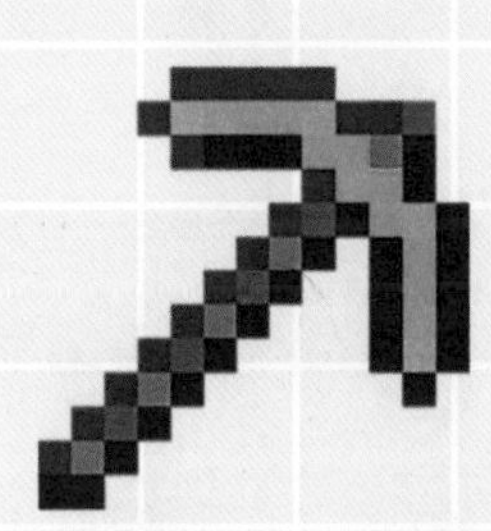

IF YOU'VE JUST STARTED, THINK SMALL. DON'T TRY TO BUILD A MANSION WITH A MOAT BEFORE NIGHTFALL!

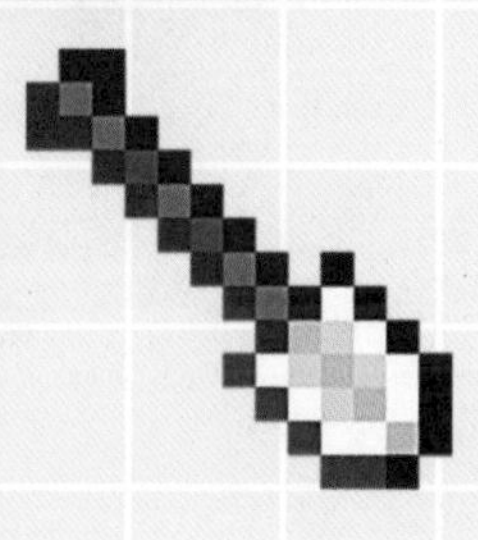

Make use of different textures. A white wall can look special by using bone blocks, white wool and quartz mixed up.

CHOOSE YOUR COLOURS CAREFULLY SO IT ALL BLENDS WELL TOGETHER.

PROVIDE MOOD LIGHTING IN YOUR HOME USING ICE OR WATER BLOCKS.

USE COPPER TO BUILD A VAULT DOOR TO PROTECT YOUR VALUABLE STUFF OR TO MAKE A SAFE ROOM.

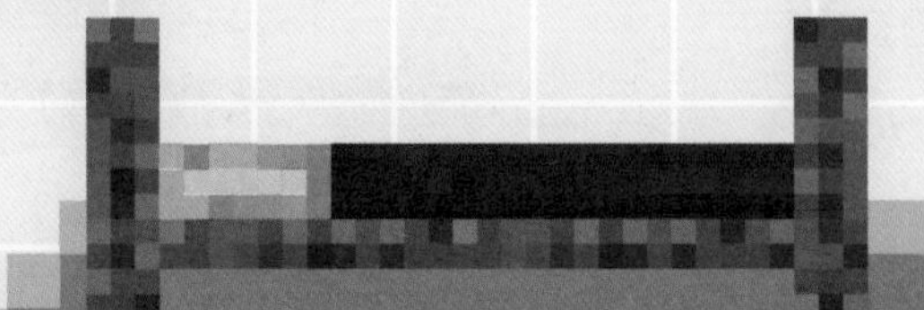

Keep your bed in a secure bunker in the centre of your home so a mob cannot prevent you from sleeping or blow up your bed.

GRID GAME

Look carefully at the grid below and work out what goes in the missing squares. No item can be repeated in any row or column.

Draw the right item in each square!

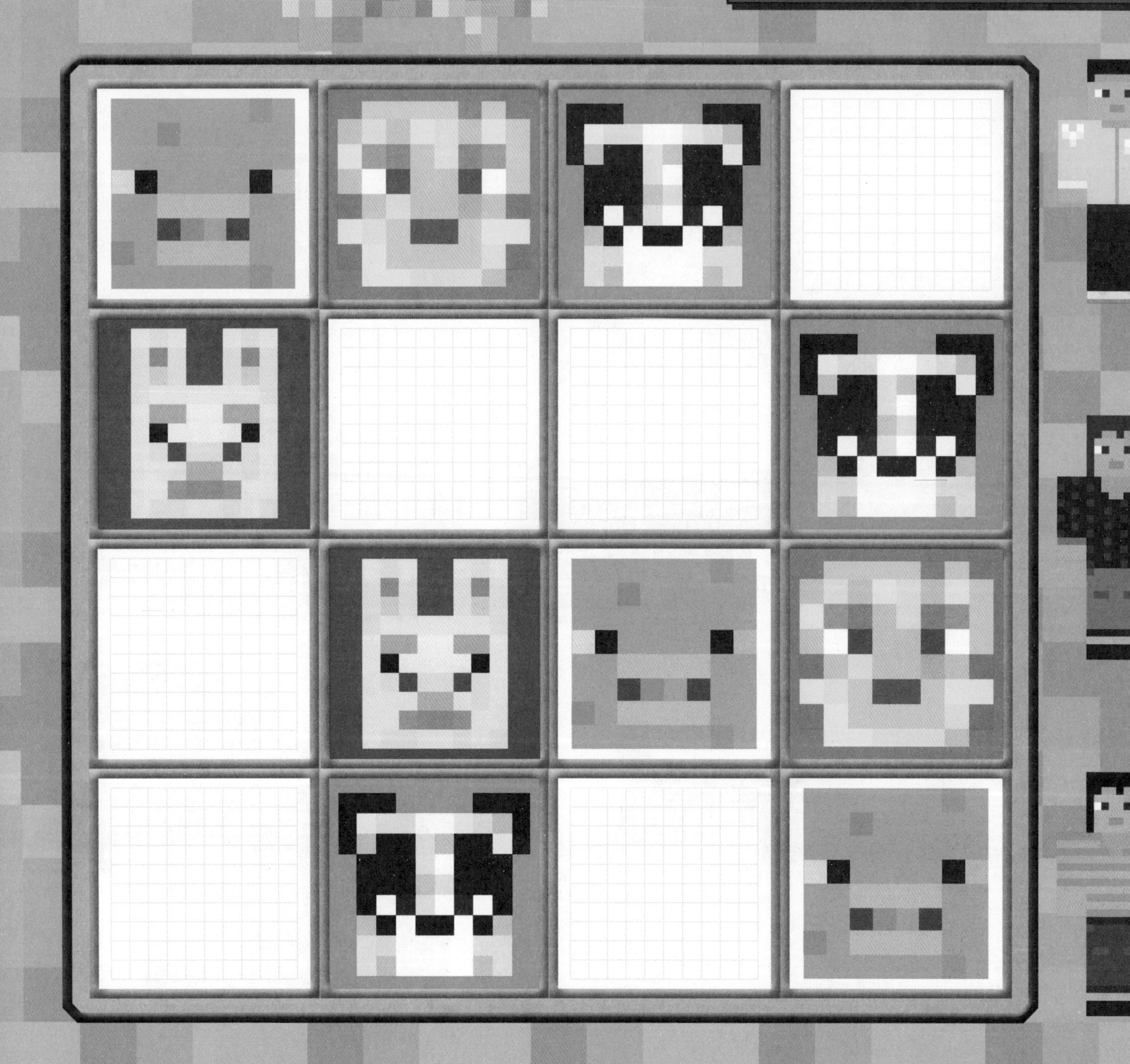

Answers on PAGE 52

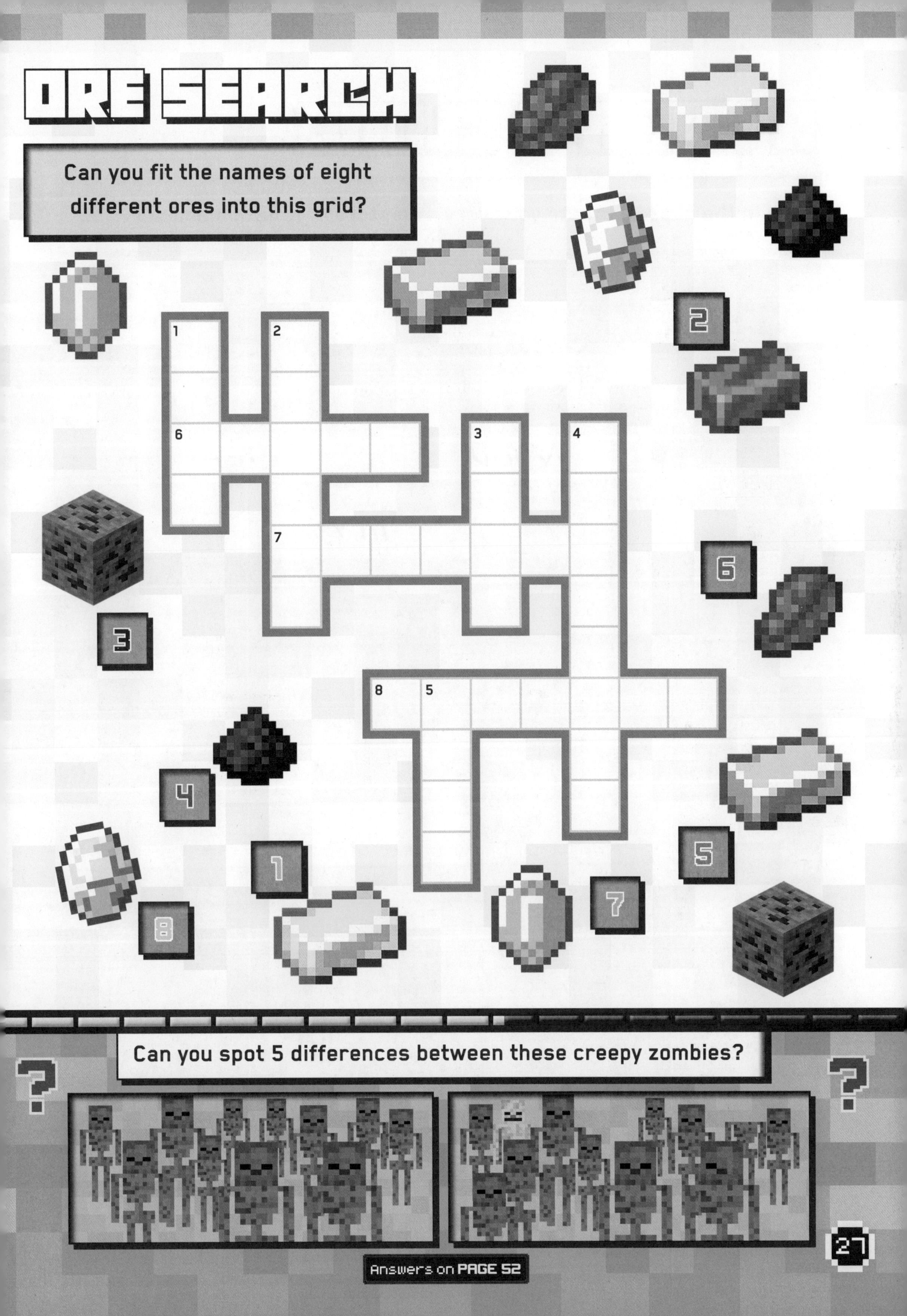
ORE SEARCH
Can you fit the names of eight different ores into this grid?
1
2
3
4
5
6
7
8
Can you spot 5 differences between these creepy zombies?
Answers on PAGE 52
27

A CREEPY CLIMB

Fill in the gaps to create your very own story of creation and survival.

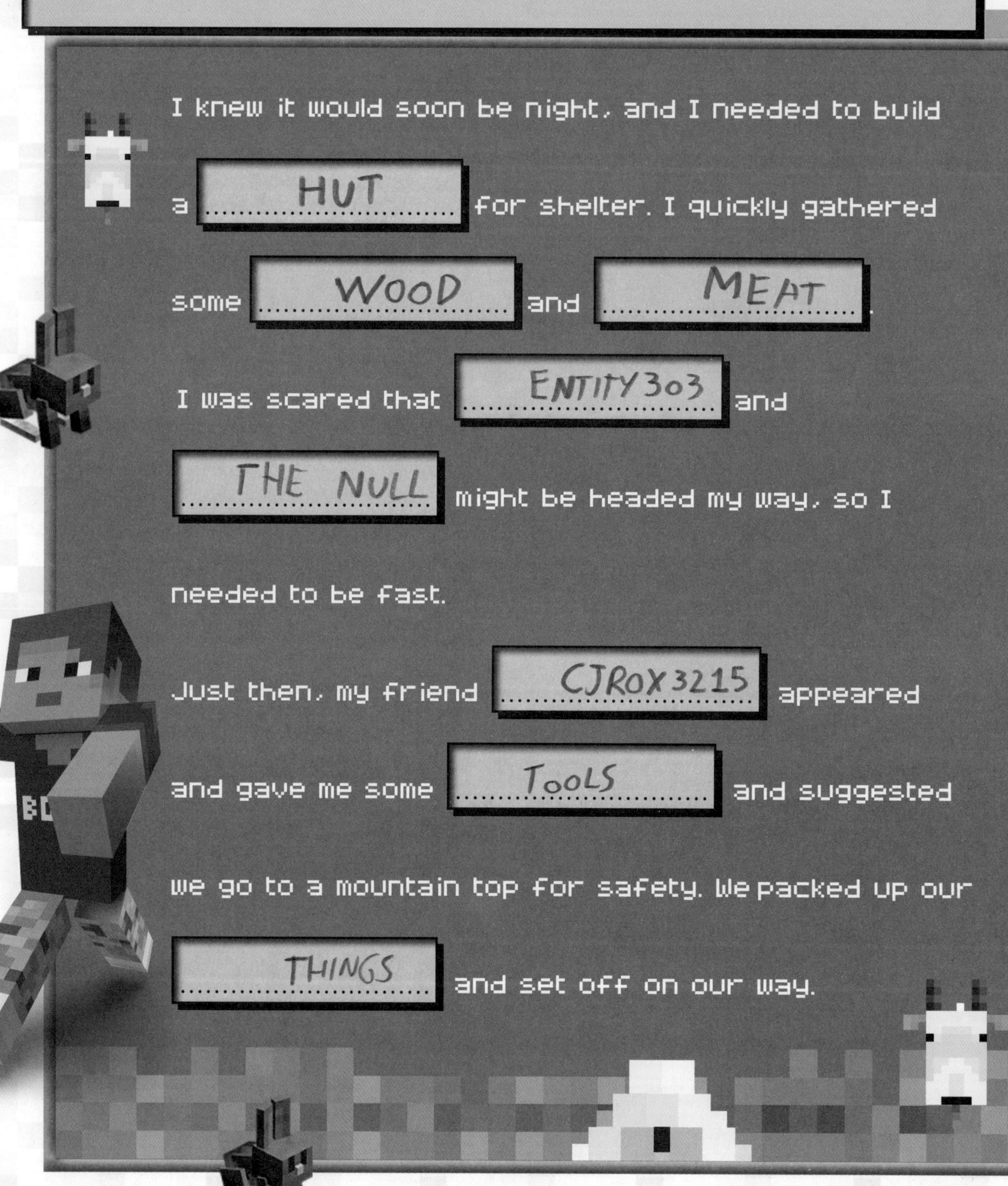

I knew it would soon be night, and I needed to build a HUT for shelter. I quickly gathered some WOOD and MEAT.

I was scared that ENTITY303 and THE NULL might be headed my way, so I needed to be fast.

Just then, my friend CJROX3215 appeared and gave me some TOOLS and suggested we go to a mountain top for safety. We packed up our THINGS and set off on our way.

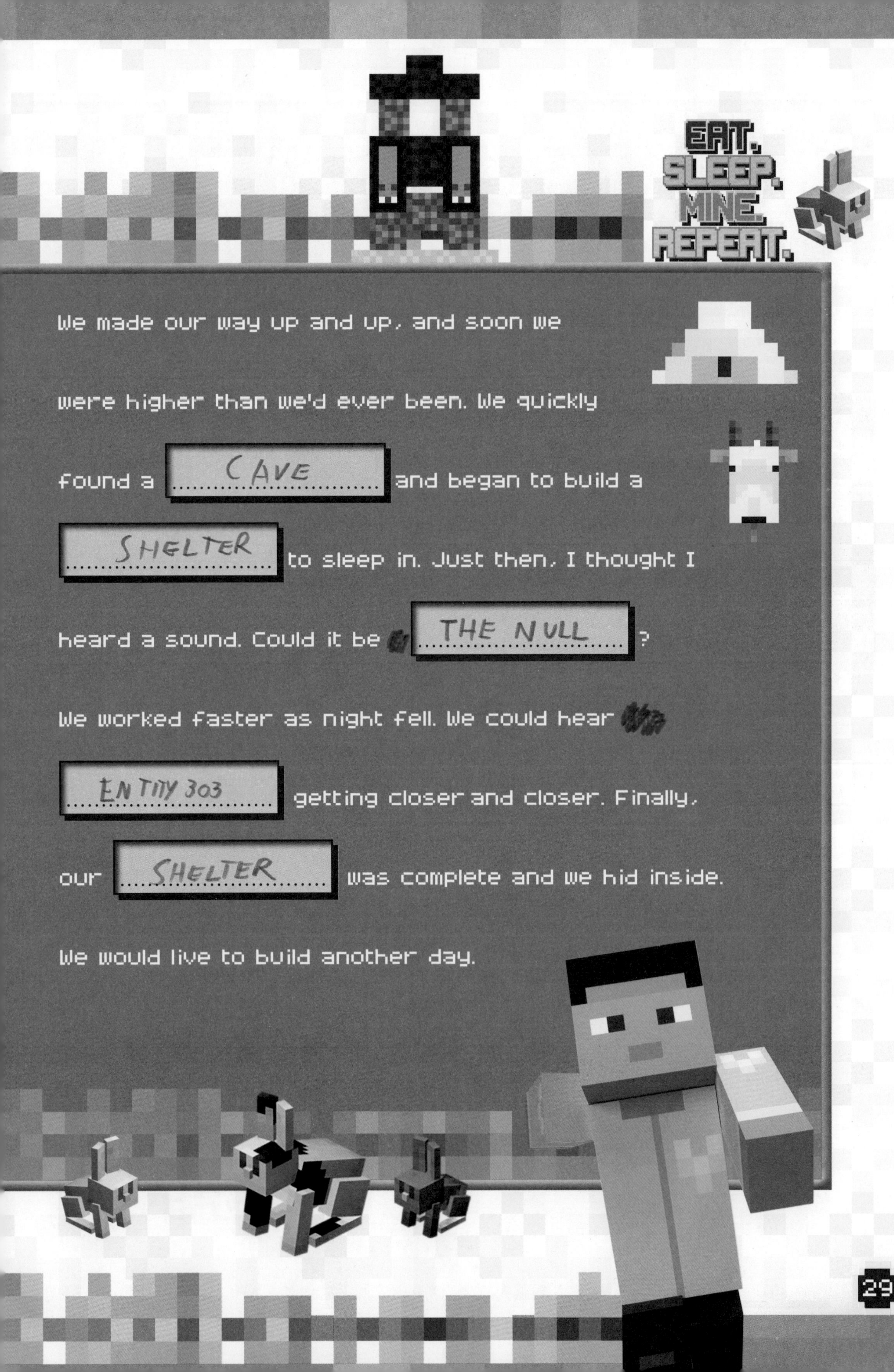

We made our way up and up, and soon we were higher than we'd ever been. We quickly found a CAVE and began to build a SHELTER to sleep in. Just then, I thought I heard a sound. Could it be THE NULL? We worked faster as night fell. We could hear ENTITY 303 getting closer and closer. Finally, our SHELTER was complete and we hid inside. We would live to build another day.

DID YOU KNOW?
HOSTILE CREATURES

YUK FACT: IF YOU KILL A SLIME IT WILL JUST MULTIPLY AND YOU'LL BE IN EVEN MORE TROUBLE!

ZOMBIES MIGHT SEEM SLOW AND PRETTY USELESS, BUT BEWARE! THEY CAN COLLABORATE AND ATTACH AS A TEAM. THEY ONLY SPAWN IN UNLIT AREAS [LIGHT LEVEL 7 OR LESS].

Guardians are hostile fish that will always spawn in or around ocean monuments.

A CREEPER COULD NEVER HURT A CAT - THEY ARE SCARED OF THEM.

The best way to defeat a hostile mob is with a melee attack. Hit them and jump back out of the way, and repeat!

If you manage to tame a spider, you'll need a saddle to ride it!

WHEN KILLED, ZOMBIES DROP PIECES OF ROTTEN FLESH. THESE CAN BE USED TO HEAL OR BREED TAME WOLVES!

SKELETONS SINK IN WATER. THEY CANNOT SWIM . . . BUT BE WARNED. THEY DO NOT DROWN.

Strays are variants of skeletons that only spawn in Ice Plains, Ice Mountains and Ice Plains Spikes. They shoot tipped arrows that inflict slowness for 30 seconds on any target!

JOURNEY HIGH AND LOW

Make your way from a dripstone cave, through a lush green cave, and up to the mountain peaks to reach your shelter, avoiding the hostile mobs along the way.

Answers on PAGE 53

MINECRAFT MAYHEM!

Use your hunting skills to track down all of the items on the list. Can you capture every mob, block, tool and weapon?

- 10 ZOMBIES
- 11 AMETHYST SHARDS
- 12 BATS
- 17 COMPASSES
- 12 SKELETONS
- 9 CREEPERS
- 20 BOTTLES OF POTION
- 3 ENDERMEN
- 23 DIAMONDS
- 5 GIRLS IN GREEN TOPS
- 6 BOYS IN RED TOPS
- 8 OCELOTS
- 7 SHOVELS
- 10 PICKAXES

HARDCORE HINT

Circle each item as you go, to make sure you've counted each one.

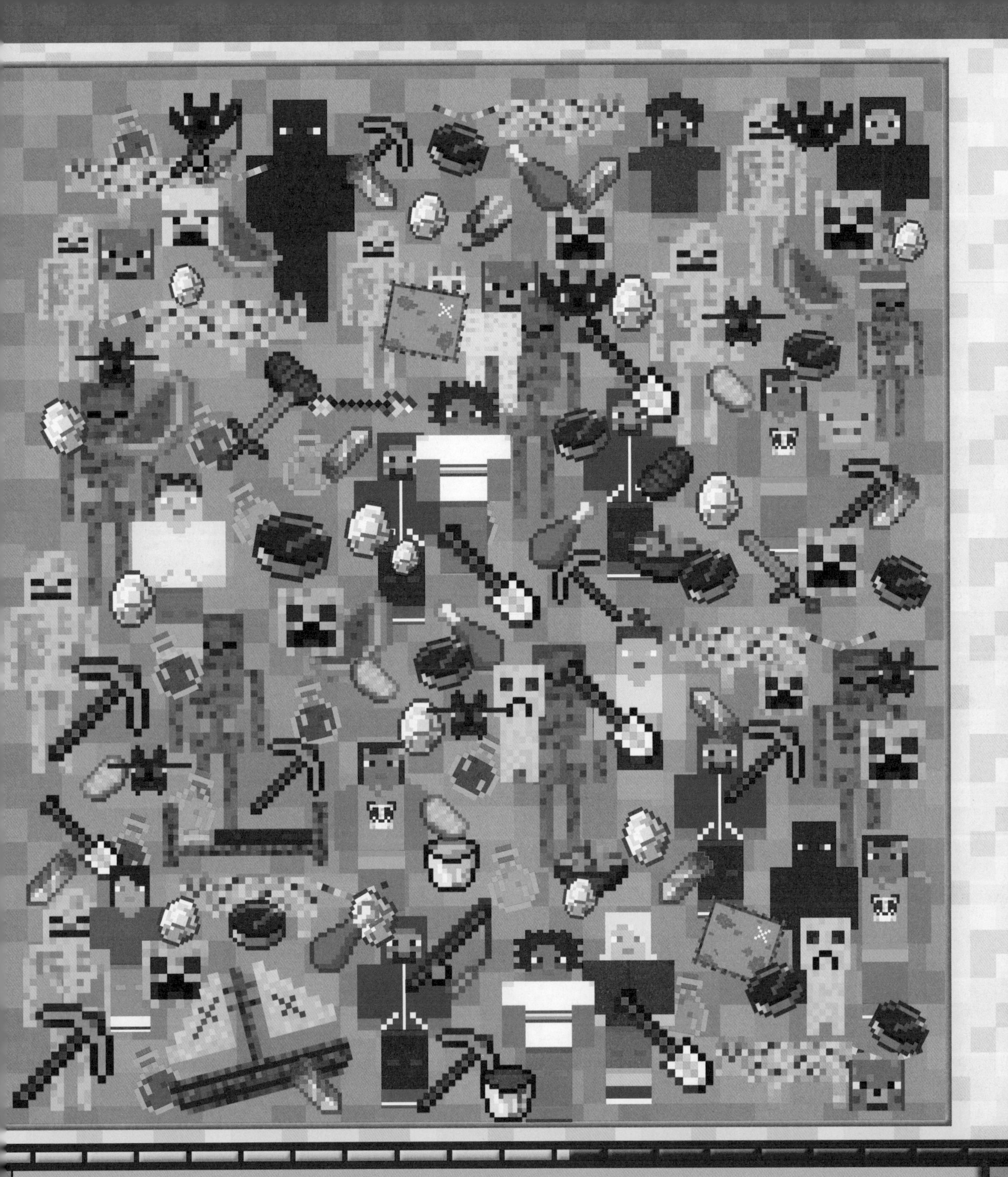

Crack the coding to reveal the type of cave that generates large copper ore blobs.

HINT: EACH NUMBER REPRESENTS A LETTER FROM THE ALPHABET (A=1, B=2, ETC.).

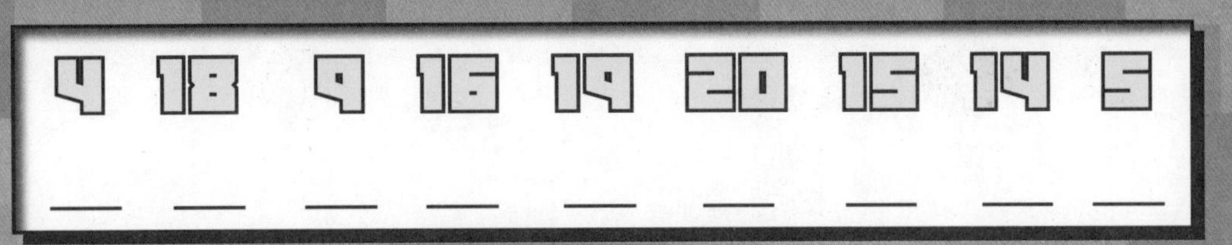

Answers on **PAGE 53**

MINING FOR WINS

Who doesn't love a bit of friendly competition? Grab a dice and a mining mate and see who can gather the most items and tame the most passive mobs!

MULTIPLAYER MODE

WHAT TO DO:

- The youngest player starts. Choose a card and take turns to roll the dice.
- Whatever number the dice lands on, circle that item on your challenge card – now it's in your inventory!
- If you land on the same number twice, it's a miss and the other player then takes their turn.
- Keep going until one player has circled all the items on their card. They win the challenge!

ACTIVATE HARDCORE MODE

Play with multiple cards at the same time!

WHO'S THE WINNER?

Count up who won the most challenges overall.

______ is the winner.

INSIDER TIPS

Who are we kidding?! YOU are the mining expert the world needs! Fill in these pages with the best things you've learned.

The most important thing to do first is

....

....

....

My top tip for surviving a long time is

....

....

....

The best way to find .... is

....

....

....

The most useful tool to have is
because
The best mob to tame is
because
My top structure-building tip is
Smash every M and C block to reveal the name of a rare tree that can generate above a lush cave biome.
M M C A C M Z C M A
C C L M C E M M A M
Answer on PAGE 53

BADDIE BANTER!

HA HA

WHY DID THE CREEPER CROSS THE ROAD?
To get to the other sssssside.

WHAT DID THE ZOMBIE SAY TO THE VILLAGER?
Nice to eat you.

DO YOU KNOW WHERE THE SCARIEST PLACE IN MINECRAFT IS?
Nether do I...

WHAT ARE THE MOST HOSTILE MOBS AT A BEACH?
The sandwitches

WHAT'S A CREEPER'S FAVOURITE DESSERT?
Ice scream!

HOW DO ZOMBIES SUCCEED IN ATTACKING YOU?
Dead-ication!

BUILD FOR THE AGES

When you use copper, your building will change over time! What copper structure will you build? Plan it out below.

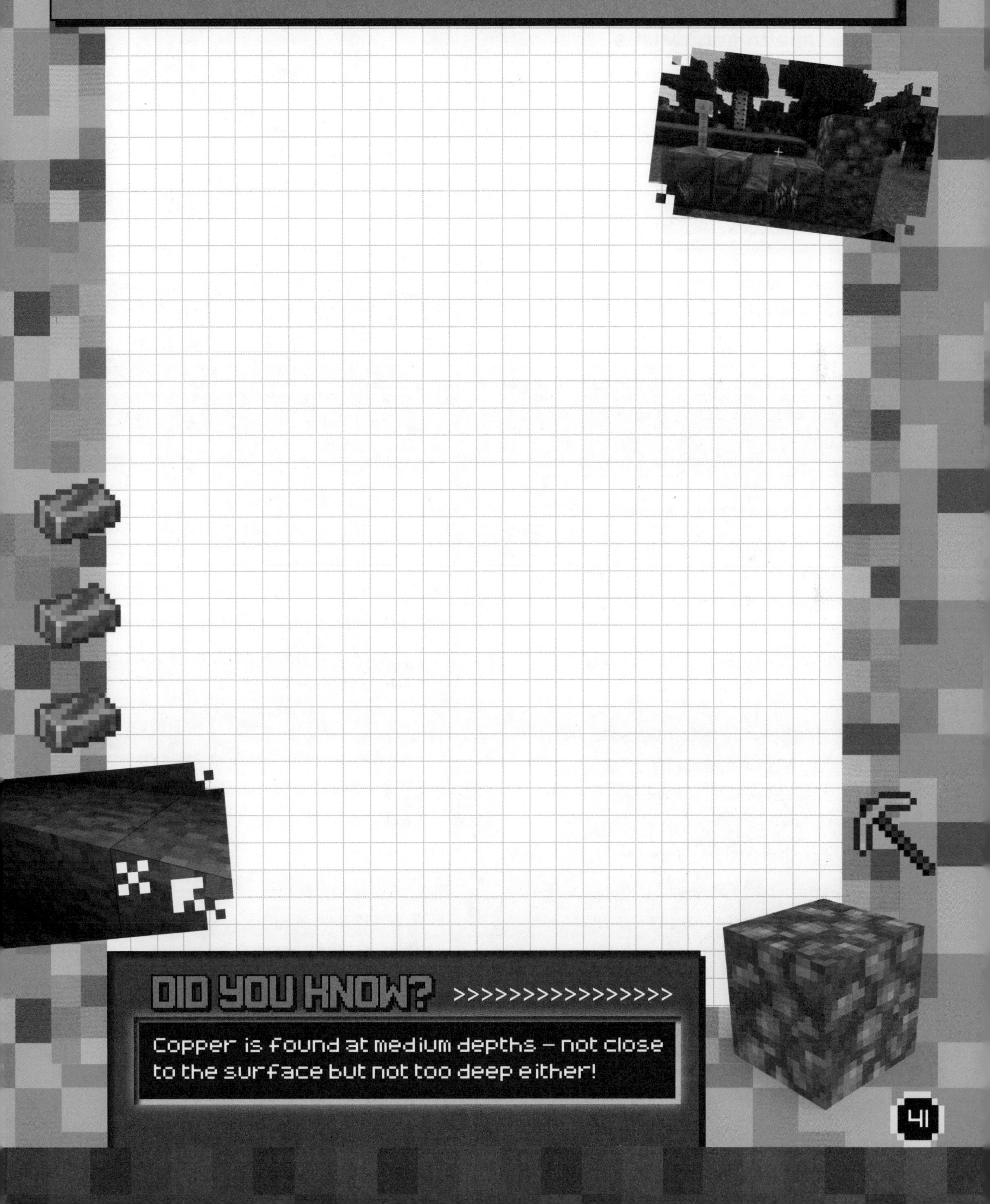

DID YOU KNOW?

>>>>>>>>>>>>>>>>>>

Copper is found at medium depths – not close to the surface but not too deep either!

HARDCORE QUIZ

It's time to get serious. This is a quiz for experts only!

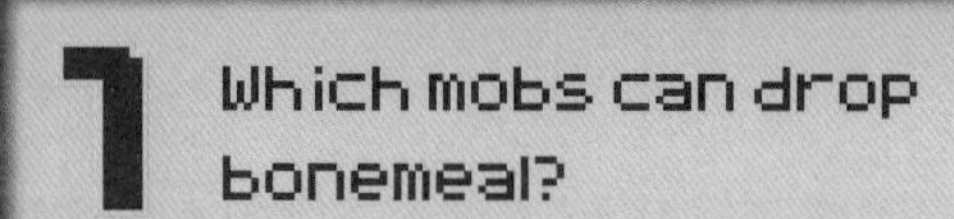

1 Which mobs can drop bonemeal?

2 One in every 10,000 times you start the game, the loading menu will spell Minecraft wrong as a joke. What does it say?

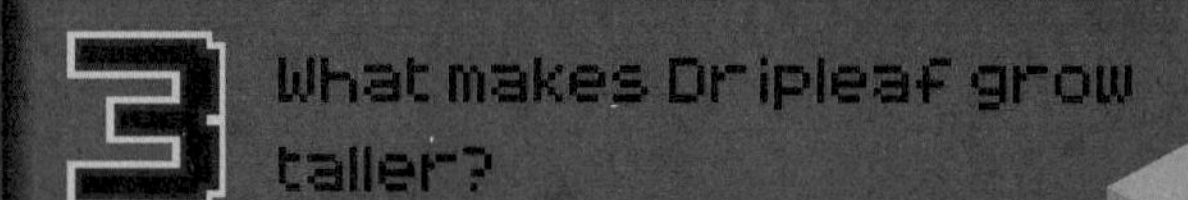

3 What makes Dripleaf grow taller?

4 What happens if you walk on Powder Snow?

5 What type of block can you place on a diagonally adjacent space from a tree sapling to make the tree instantly grow to full size?

6 What is Moss Carpet crafted from?

7 What happens if you get too close to a goat?

8 What light level do candles have?

9 What was the name of the 1.18 update?

10 What do donkeys eat in Minecraft?

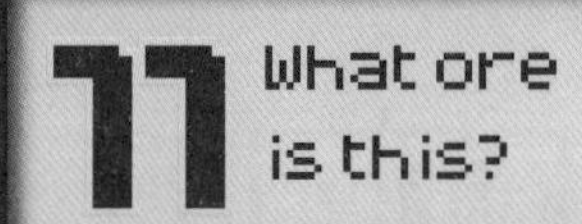

11 What ore is this?

12 What should you give to two adult foxes to make their baby fox trust you?

13 Where in a Minecraft village can you find a Blast Furnace?

14 How many blocks away can you hear mobs coming [except Creepers of course]?

15 What material can be smelted into blocks of glass?

16 What are the two main blocks used for repairing items?

17 Azalea trees can indicate that what type of cave lies below?

18 Stalactites in Dripstone Caves drip water, but they also drip something else that can be collected in a cauldron. What is it?

19 Any set of mountain blocks above Y-level 170 results in which biomes?

20 If a Charged Creeper kills a Skeleton, what three things does the Skeleton drop?

HOW MANY DID YOU GET RIGHT?

0–3 GAME OVER!

4–6 SURVIVING

7–8 THRIVING

9–10 EXPERT ALERT!

Quick quiz! Circle TRUE or FALSE for these statements.

1. If you milk a mooshroom you get mushroom soup. TRUE | FALSE
2. Endermen speak backwards English. TRUE | FALSE
3. Zombies will give you flowers if you stand next to them. TRUE | FALSE

Answers on PAGE 53

A PLACE FOR SURVIVAL

One way to survive hardcore mode is to build an intricate cave world where you can eat, sleep, mine and hide. Plan out your cave system on this pixel grid, and list out the key items you'll collect in order to survive.

HARDCORE HINT

Have access to a stack of cobblestone. It's perfect for crafting an impromptu base if you're not home when night starts to fall.

HARDCORE HINT

Have back-ups of everything – tools, weapons and armour especially.

HARDCORE HINT

Ensure all areas are well-lit.

KEY ITEMS

HARDCORE HINT

Include multiple exits and entrances for each area, so you don't get trapped!

WHO'S THAT MOB?

There are some hostile mobs lurking in the darkness. Can you work out which they are? Match each name to its close-up.

A

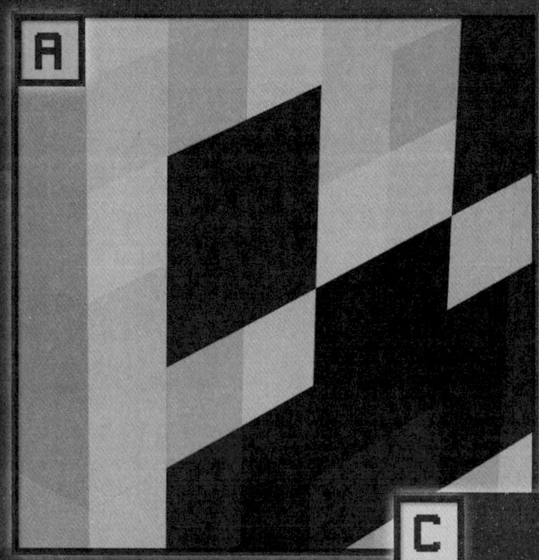

GUARDIAN

B

C

SLIME

SKELETON

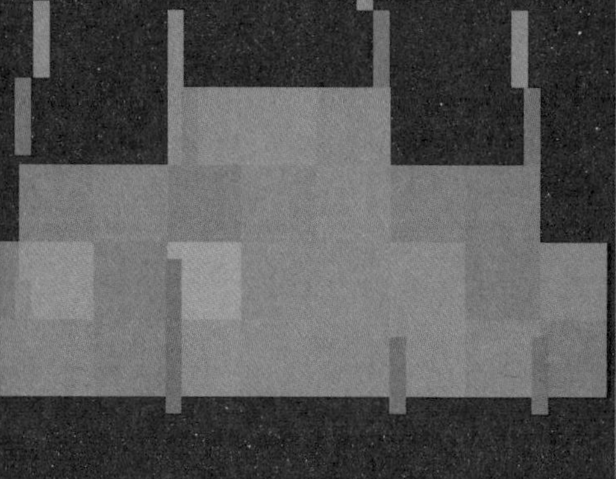

D

ZOMBIE

E

F

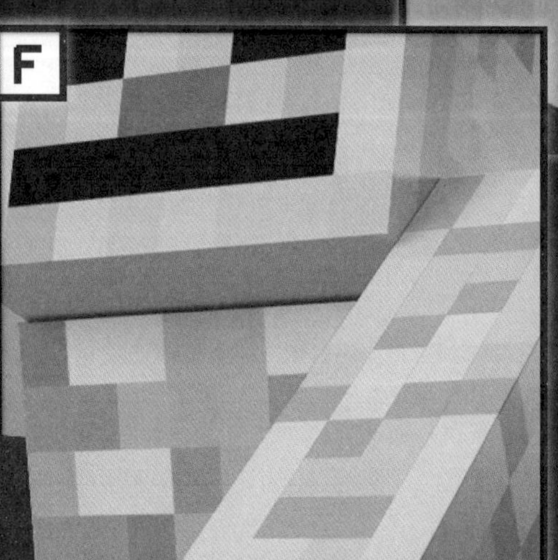

SILVERFISH

CREEPER

Answers on PAGE 53

PATH TO THE PICKAXE

A pickaxe is essential to mine ores, rock, rock-based blocks and metal-based blocks. You definitely need one! Which path will take you there?

A

B

C

D

Answers on PAGE 53

BUILD PATTERNS

Use your expert eye to spot the build patterns being made by these blocks. Colour in the missing one in each row.

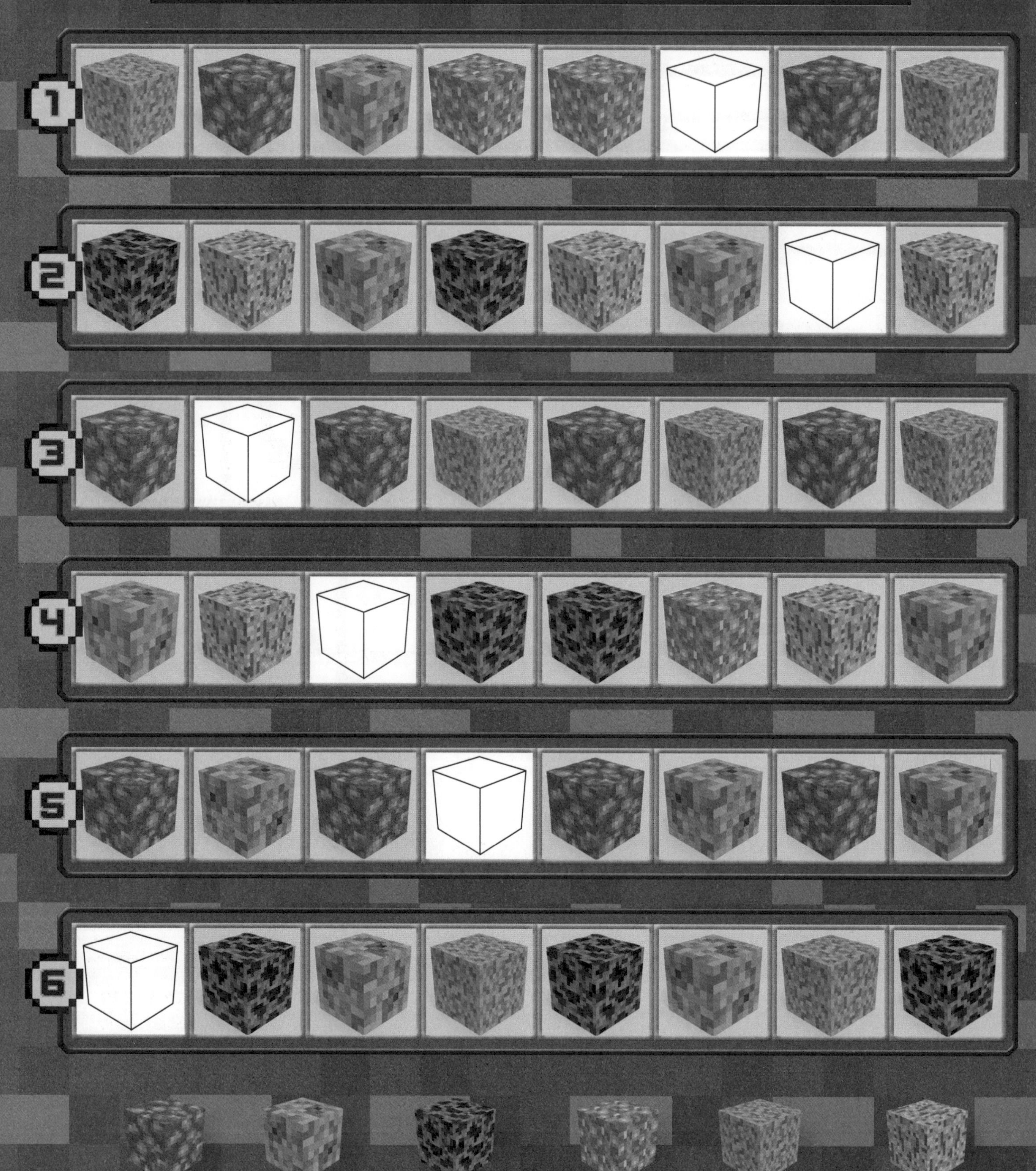

Answers on **PAGE 53**

INVENTORY BUG

Oh no! There's been a glitch in your inventory! Can you spot and circle the 10 things that have changed?

Add up these blocks to complete the builds! Each block should contain the total of the two blocks below it.

Answers on PAGE 53

FIX THE GLITCH

Oops there's a glitch in the game and these items are hard to make out. Can you name each one?

A

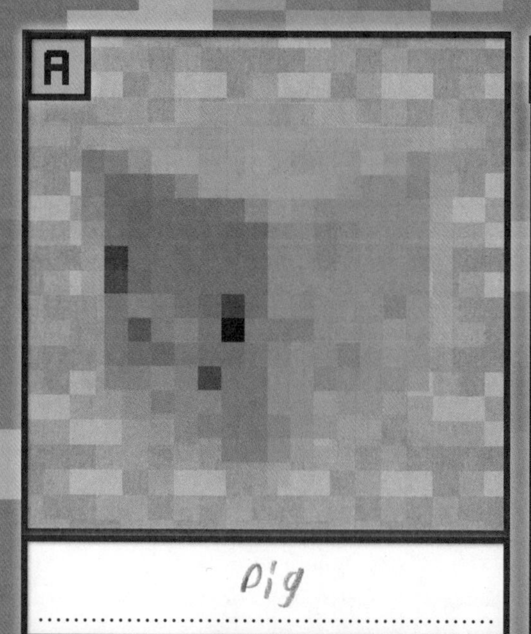

pig

B

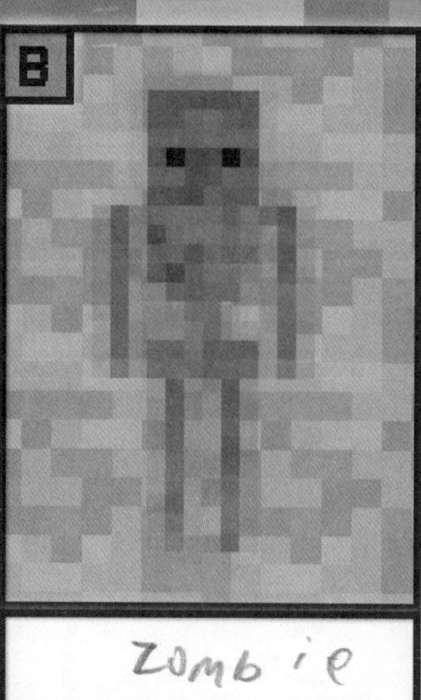

zombie

C

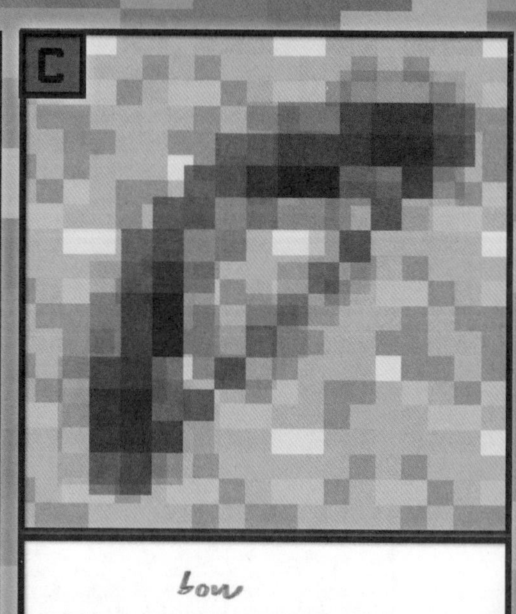

bow

D

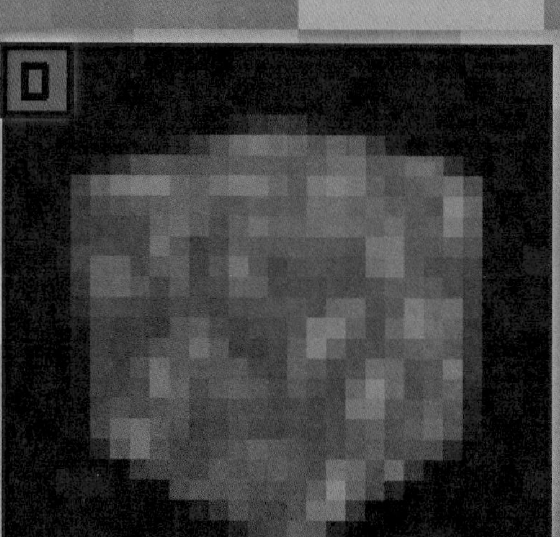

raw copper

E

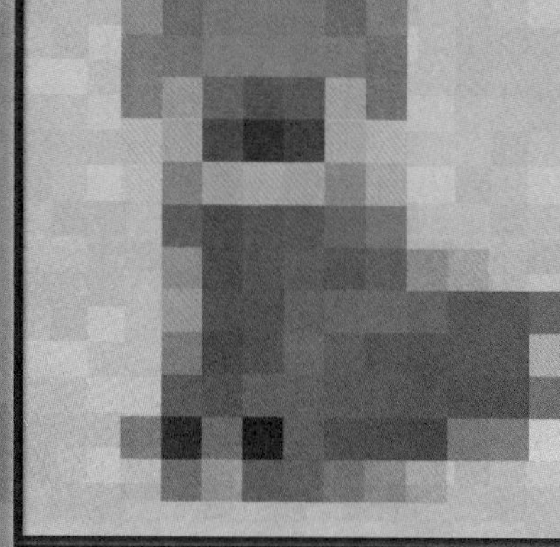

fox

F

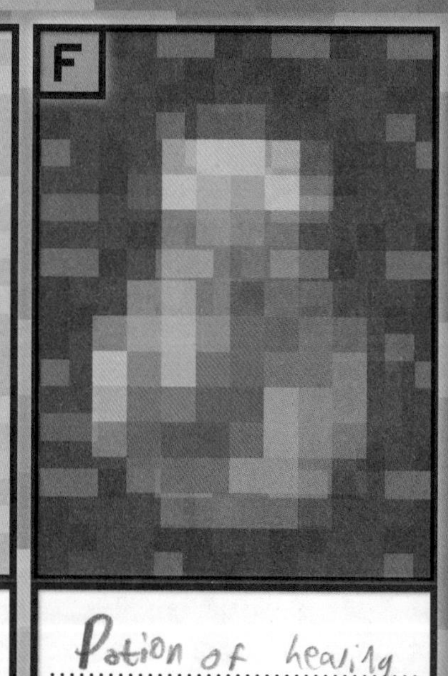

Potion of healing

ANSWERS ON PAGE 53

MY BEST BLOCKS

Now you've finished building your knowledge and testing your epic blocking skills, fill out your best bits on this page so you remember them.

THE MOST BLOCK-BUSTING TIP I LEARNED:

....

MY FAVOURITE JOKE:

....

THE ACTIVITY I WAS BEST AT:

....

THE ACTIVITY I COMPLETED THE QUICKEST:

....

THE MULTIPLAYER MODE GAME I WAS BEST AT:

....

A NEW BUILDING PROJECT I PLANNED:

....

SOMETHING I'M GOING TO DO IN MY WORLD RIGHT NOW!

....

What hostile mob is lurking under the water?

ANSWERS ON PAGE 53

ANSWERS

PAGES 10 – 11:

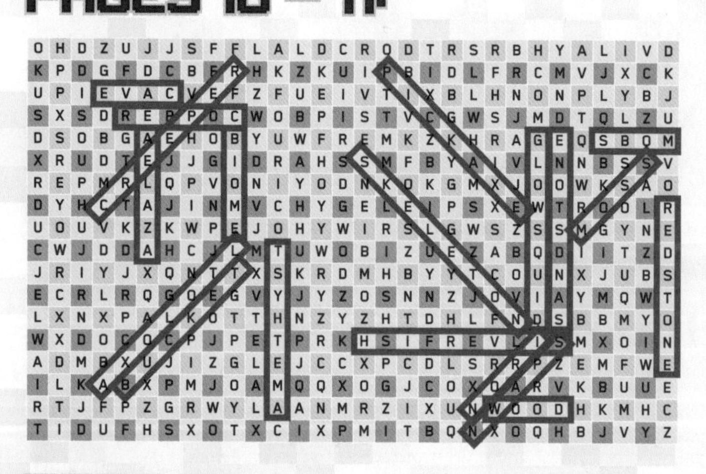

PAGE 13:

AXOLOTL.

PAGE 14:

DIAMOND ORE.

PAGE 20:

PAGE 21:

1. DONKEY, **2.** HORSE, **3.** WOLF.

PAGE 26:

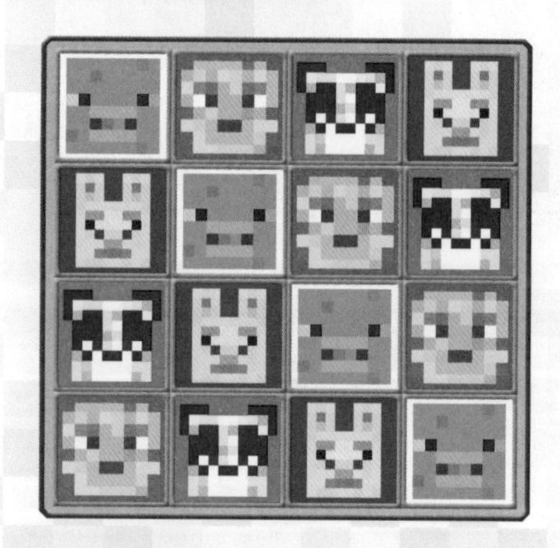

PAGE 27:

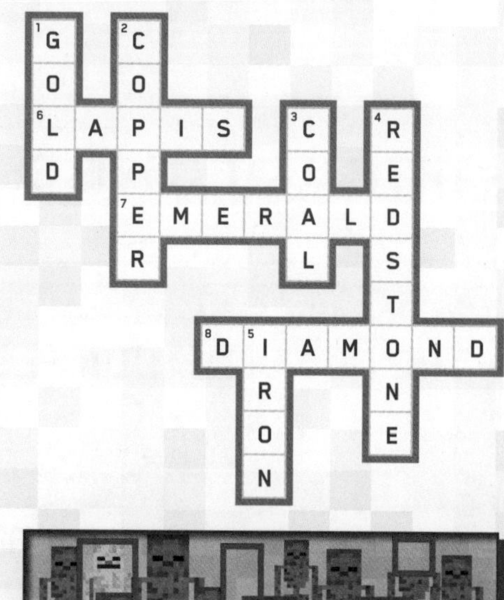

PAGES 22 – 23:

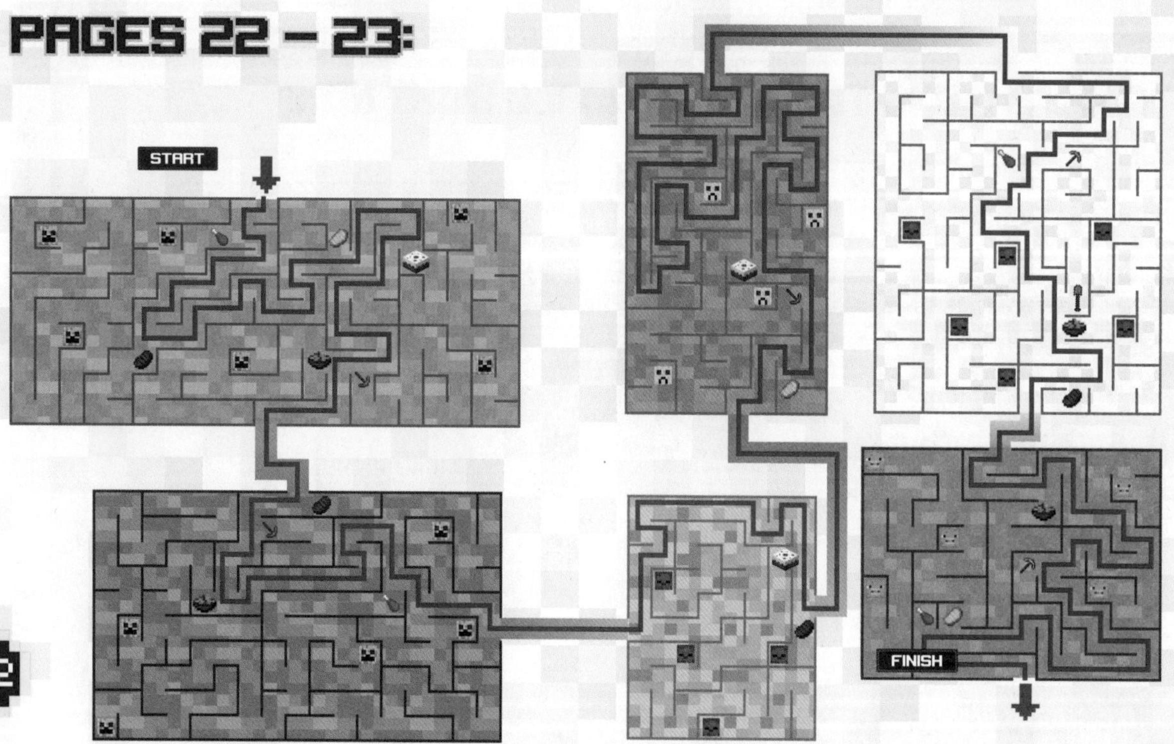

PAGES 32 – 33:

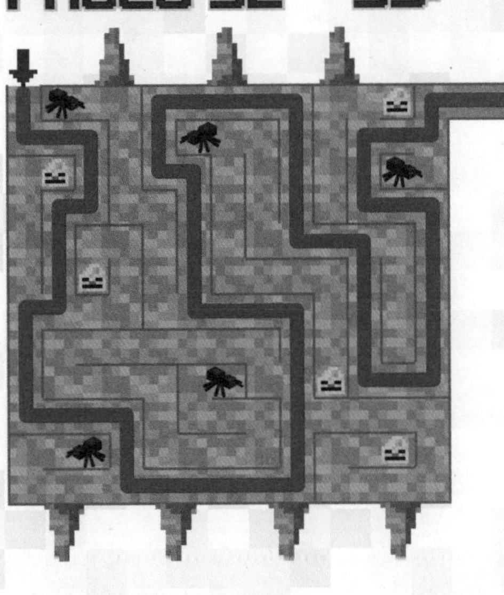

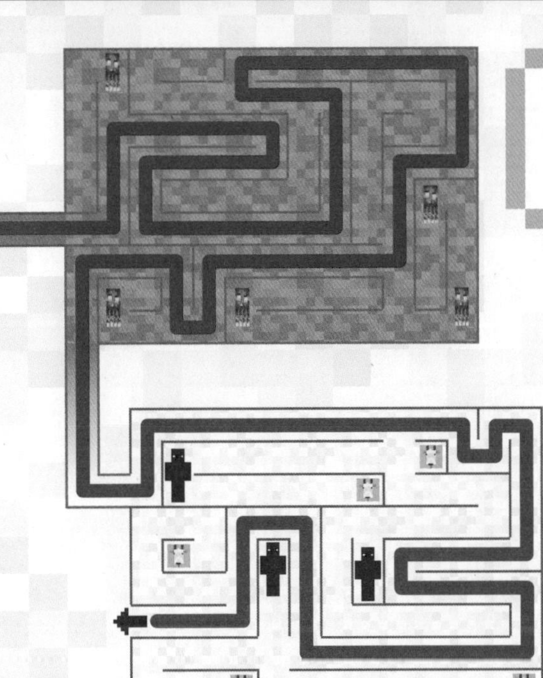

PAGE 35:

DRIPSTONE.

PAGE 39:

AZALEA.

PAGES 42 – 43:

1. Fish, **2.** Mincecraft, **3.** Bonemeal, **4.** You sink into it, **5.** A glass block, **6.** Moss blocks, **7.** It tries to ram you, **8.** 3, **9.** Caves & Cliffs, **10.** Sugar, **11.** Copper, **12.** Sweet berries, **13.** Armorer's house, **14.** 16, **15.** Sand, **16.** Grindstone and Anvil, **17.** Lush Cave, **18.** Lava, **19.** Jagged Peaks or Frozen Peaks, **20.** Skulls, bones and arrows.

1 - TRUE, **2** - TRUE, **3** - FALSE

PAGE 46:

A - Creeper, **B** - Zombie, **C** - Silverfish, **D** - Guardian, **E** - Slime, **F** - Skeleton.

PAGE 47:

D IS THE CORRECT PATH.

PAGE 48:

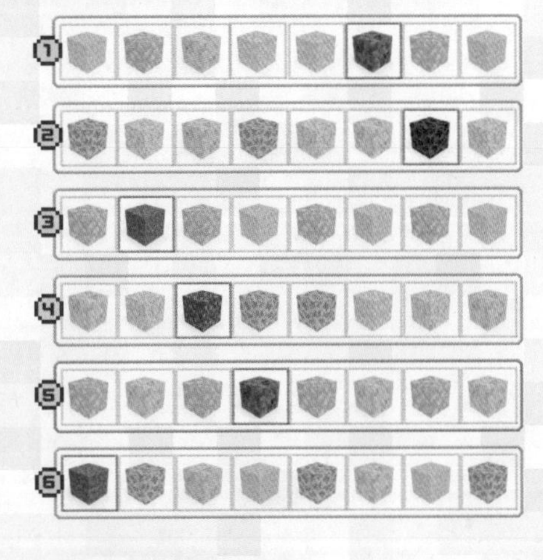

PAGE 49:

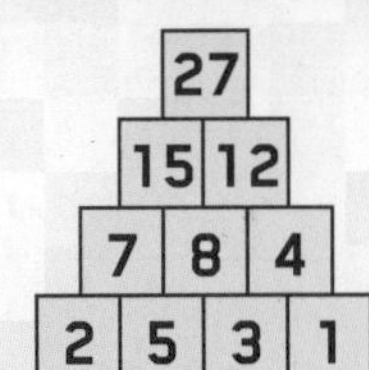

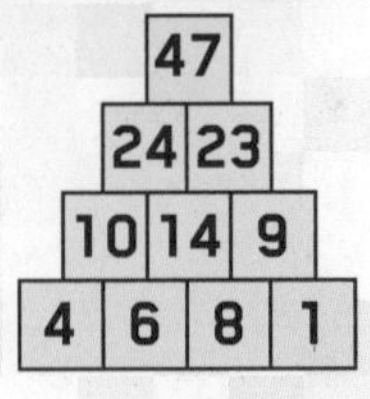

PAGE 50:

A - Pig, **B** - Zombie, **C** - Bow, **D** - Copper Block, **E** - Fox, **F** - Potion.

PAGE 51:

GUARDIAN.

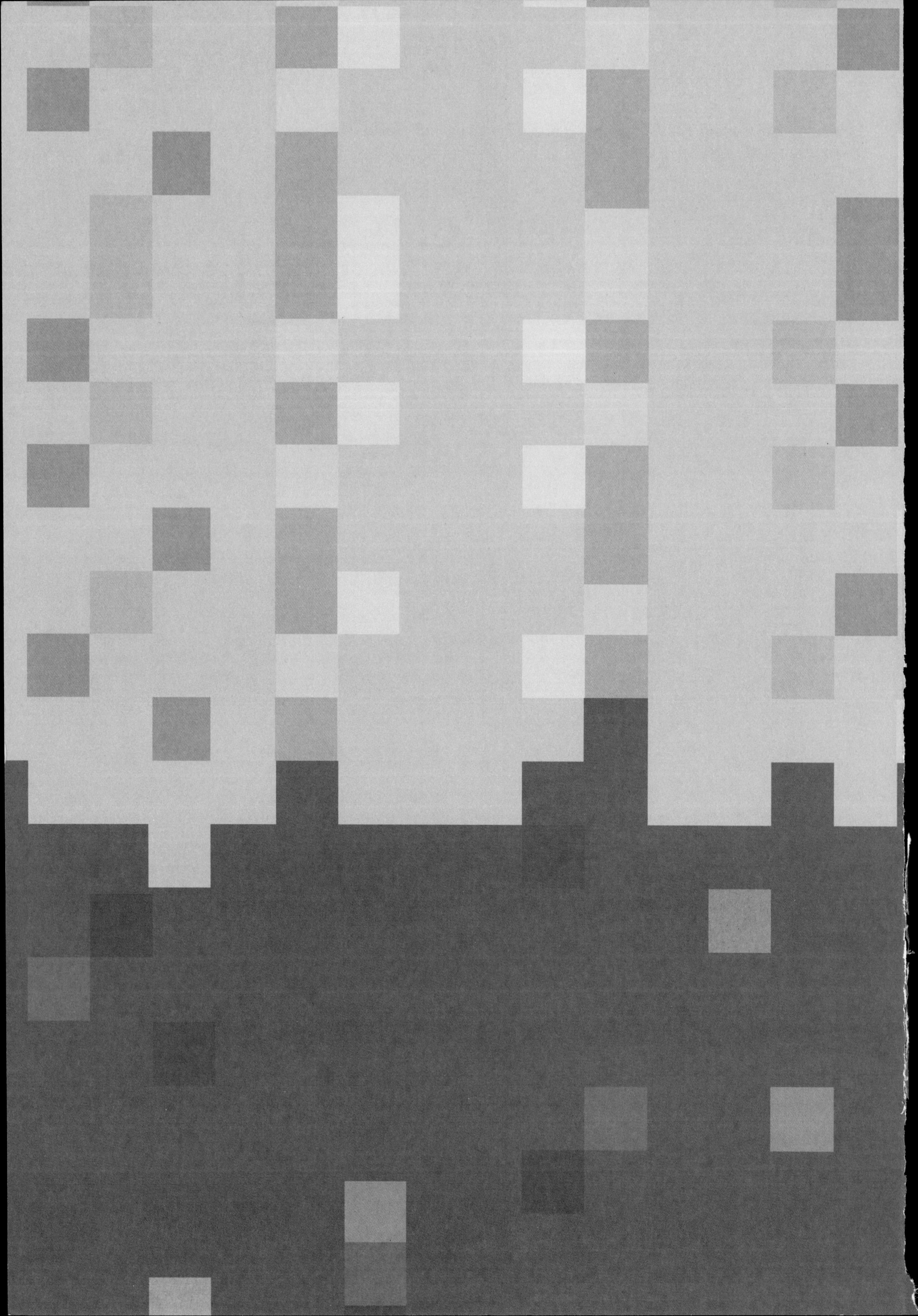